Theory Paper Grade 6 2011 A

Duration 3 hours

Candidates should answer all FIVE questions.
Write your answers on this paper – no others will be accepted.
Answers must be written clearly and neatly – otherwise marks may be lost.

TOTAL MARKS
100

1 Answer ONE section only, (a) or (b).

15

EITHER

(a) Indicate ONE chord at each of the places marked ∗ to accompany the following melody. You may do so by writing roman numerals or any other recognized method of notation between the staves, OR by writing notes on the staves which provide a proper harmonic structure; but use only ONE of these methods.

[Andante]   Old English Melody

OR

(b) Complete the bass line and add a suitable figured bass as necessary, *from the final quaver of bar 2*, at the places marked ∗ in this passage. If you wish to use a $\frac{5}{3}$ chord, leave the space under the asterisk blank, but $\frac{5}{3}$ chords *must* be shown when used as part of a $\frac{6}{4}\,\frac{5}{3}$ progression or when chromatic alteration is required.

M. Greene, 'Acquaint thyself with God' (adapted)

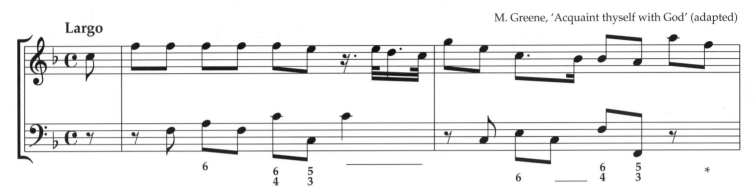

2 Writing for four-part voices (SATB) or keyboard, realize this figured bass. Assume that all chords are $\frac{5}{3}$ unless otherwise shown.

3 EITHER

(a) Continue this opening to form a complete melody for unaccompanied oboe. It should end with a modulation to the relative major and should be between eight and ten bars long. Add performance directions as appropriate and write the complete melody on the staves below.

OR

(b) Continue this opening for unaccompanied bassoon to make a complete piece of not less than eight bars in length. You may make any modulation or modulations that you wish, or none if you prefer. Add performance directions as appropriate and write the complete melody on the staves below.

4 Look at the extract printed opposite, which is from a keyboard suite, and then answer the questions below.

25

(a) Give the meaning of **Lentement**. .... (2)

(b) Identify the chords marked * in bars 3 and 5 by writing on the dotted lines below. Use either words or symbols. Indicate the position of each chord, show whether it is major, minor, augmented or diminished, and name the prevailing key.

Bar 3 ....

Bar 5 .... } Key: .... (7)

(c) Mark **clearly** on the score, using the appropriate capital letter for identification, one example of each of the following. Also give the bar number(s) of each of your answers. The first answer is given.

In bars 1–12

A a pair of grace notes in the right-hand part (circle the notes concerned). Bar .....9.....

B an imperfect cadence in the relative major key. Bars .... (2)

C a melodic interval of a diminished 7th in the top line of the right-hand part (circle the notes concerned). Bars .... (2)

D a harmonic interval of an augmented 4th in the left-hand part (circle the notes concerned). Bar .... (2)

(d) Write out in full the top right-hand part of bar 19 as you think it should be played.

(3)

(e) Give the full names of the notes of melodic decoration (e.g. lower auxiliary note) marked **X**, **Y** and **Z** in bars 2, 3 and 15.

X (left hand, bar 2)   .... (2)

Y (right hand, bar 3)   .... (2)

Z (right hand, bar 15)   .... (2)

(f) From the list below, underline the name of the most likely composer of this extract.

Beethoven   Handel   Chopin   Mozart (1)

5 Look at the extract printed opposite, which is from an overture by Mendelssohn, and
then answer the questions below.

(a) Give the meaning of:

con moto .... (2)

arco (e.g. bar 2, violas) .... (2)

(b) Write out the parts for clarinets and horns in bars 5–6 as they would sound at concert pitch
and using the given clefs.

(4)

(3)

(c) The opening motif played by the first clarinet (marked [   ]) is later imitated
by other instruments. Name three instruments *other than the clarinet* that play this motif and
give the bar numbers in which each imitation occurs.

Instrument .... Bars .... (2)

Instrument .... Bars .... (2)

Instrument .... Bars .... (2)

(d) Mark **clearly** on the score, using the appropriate capital letter for identification, one example
of each of the following. Also give the bar number of each of your answers. The first answer
is given.

In bars 1–4

A a place where the second horn and cellos
sound a note in unison (circle the notes concerned). Bar ....1....

B a place where a string player must play an open string (circle the note concerned). Bar .... (2)

C a harmonic interval of a major 3rd between two
single-reed instruments (circle the notes concerned). Bar .... (2)

(e) Describe fully the numbered and bracketed harmonic intervals *sounding* in each of the
following bars:

1 bar 3, violas and second bassoon .... (2)

2 bar 8, double basses and second clarinet .... (2)

BLANK PAGE

Theory Paper Grade 6 2011 B

Duration 3 hours

Candidates should answer all FIVE questions.
Write your answers on this paper – no others will be accepted.
Answers must be written clearly and neatly – otherwise marks may be lost.

TOTAL MARKS
100

1 Answer **ONE** section only, (a) or (b).

15

EITHER

(a) Indicate **ONE** chord at each of the places marked * to accompany the following melody. You may do so by writing roman numerals or any other recognized method of notation between the staves, **OR** by writing notes on the staves which provide a proper harmonic structure; but use only **ONE** of these methods.

Corelli, Preludio, Sonata No. 10, Op. 5 (adapted)

OR

(b) Complete the bass line and add a suitable figured bass as necessary, *from the second beat of bar 4*, at the places marked ∗ in this passage. If you wish to use a $\frac{5}{3}$ chord, leave the space under the asterisk blank, but $\frac{5}{3}$ chords *must* be shown when used as part of a $\frac{6}{4}\frac{5}{3}$ progression or when chromatic alteration is required.

J. B. de Boismortier, Sonata Terza, Op. 19 (adapted)

2 Writing for four-part voices (SATB) or keyboard, realize this figured bass. Assume that all chords are $\frac{5}{3}$ unless otherwise shown.

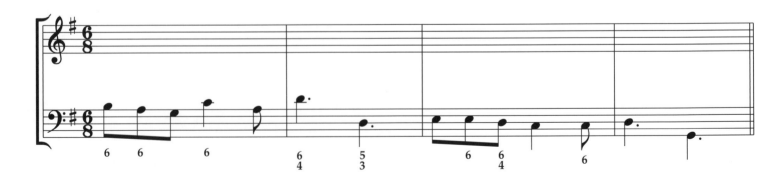

3 EITHER

(a) Continue this opening to form a complete melody for unaccompanied cello. It should end with a modulation to the relative major and should be between eight and ten bars long. Add performance directions as appropriate and write the complete melody on the staves below.

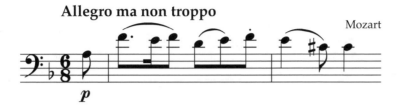

OR

(b) Continue this opening for unaccompanied clarinet (at concert pitch) to make a complete piece of not less than eight bars in length. You may make any modulation or modulations that you wish, or none if you prefer. Add performance directions as appropriate and write the complete melody on the staves below.

Andante espressivo

cantabile

poco più mosso

etc.

4 Look at the extract printed opposite, which is from a piano piece by Grieg, and then answer the questions below.

25

(a) Give the full names of the notes of melodic decoration (e.g. upper auxiliary note) marked **X**, **Y** and **Z** in the right-hand part of bars 4, 7 and 11.

X (bar 4) .... (2)

Y (bar 7) .... (2)

Z (bar 11) .... (2)

(b) Identify the chords marked ＊ in bars 2 and 9 (bracketed) by writing on the dotted lines below. Use either words or symbols. Indicate the position of each chord, show whether it is major, minor, augmented or diminished, and name the prevailing key.

Bar 2 .... Key .... (4)

Bar 9 .... Key .... (4)

(c) Mark **clearly** on the score, using the appropriate capital letter for identification, one example of each of the following. Also give the bar number(s) of each of your answers. The first answer is given.

From bar 9 onwards

A syncopation in the right-hand part. Bar .....9......

B a melodic interval of a diminished 5th in the left-hand part (circle the notes concerned). Bar .... (2)

C a decorated perfect cadence in the tonic key. Bars .... (2)

D arpeggiation in the right-hand part. Bar .... (2)

E melodic imitation between the hands within a bar. Bar .... (2)

(d) Write out in full the top line of the right-hand part of bar 12 as you think it should be played.

(3)

5 Look at the extract printed on pages 17–18, which is from an orchestral suite by A. Tcherepnin, and then answer the questions below.

(a) Give the meaning of:

Mesto .... (2)

pizz. (bar 1, cellos) .... (2)

a 2 (e.g. bar 5, clarinets) .... (2)

(b) (i) Using the blank stave at the foot of page 18, write out the parts for clarinets in bar 6 as they would sound at concert pitch and using the given clef. (3)

(ii) The notes printed below are written for the first and second horns shortly before the extract begins. Write out the parts (for horns in F) as they would sound at concert pitch and using the given clef.

(4)

(c) Complete the following statements:

(i) The motif played by the third horn in bars 3–4 is repeated in bars 7–8 where it is also

played by the .... and the .... (2)

(ii) Two differences between the third horn part in bars 3–4 and its repeat by the same

instrument in bars 7–8 are the .... (1)

and the .... (1)

(d) Describe fully the numbered and bracketed harmonic intervals on the first beat of each of the following bars, *sounding* between:

1 bar 4, first bassoon and second flute .... (2)

2 bar 5, double basses and first horn .... (2)

(e) Answer TRUE or FALSE to the following statements:

(i) In bars 5–6 the first violins and violas
play the same notes sounding an octave apart. .... (2)

(ii) In bars 1–4 the largest melodic interval in a woodwind part is a minor 3rd. .... (2)

(b) (i)

bar 6   Clarinets

Theory Paper Grade 6   2011   C

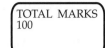
DO NOT PHOTOCOPY
© MUSIC

Duration 3 hours

Candidates should answer all FIVE questions.
Write your answers on this paper – no others will be accepted.
Answers must be written clearly and neatly – otherwise marks may be lost.

TOTAL MARKS
100

1 Answer **ONE** section only, (a) or (b).

15

EITHER

(a) Indicate **ONE** chord at each of the places marked * to accompany the following melody. You may do so by writing roman numerals or any other recognized method of notation between the staves, **OR** by writing notes on the staves which provide a proper harmonic structure; but use only **ONE** of these methods.

OR

(b) Complete the bass line and add a suitable figured bass as necessary, *from the first beat of bar 2*, at the places marked ∗ in this passage. If you wish to use a $\frac{5}{3}$ chord, leave the space under the asterisk blank, but $\frac{5}{3}$ chords *must* be shown when used as part of a $\frac{6}{4}\frac{5}{3}$ progression or when chromatic alteration is required.

Andante larghetto

Handel, Aria from *Hercules* (adapted)

2 Writing for four-part voices (SATB) or keyboard, realize this figured bass.
Assume that all chords are $\frac{5}{3}$ unless otherwise shown.

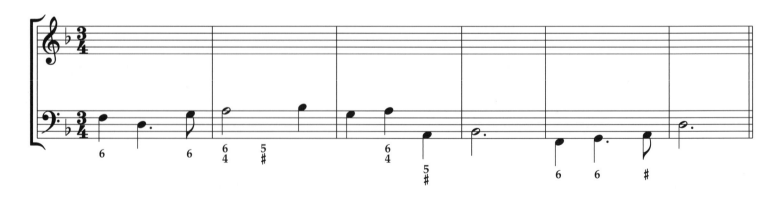

3 EITHER

(a) Continue this opening to form a complete melody for unaccompanied violin. It should end with a modulation to the subdominant and should be between eight and ten bars long. Add performance directions as appropriate and write the complete melody on the staves below.

Allegro moderato   Haydn

OR

(b) Continue this opening for unaccompanied trombone to make a complete piece of not less than eight bars in length. You may make any modulation or modulations that you wish, or none if you prefer. Add performance directions as appropriate and write the complete melody on the staves below.

Andante

Menuetto

4 Look at the extract printed opposite, which is from a piano sonata, and then answer the questions below.

25

(a) Identify the chords marked * in bars 13 and 30 by writing on the dotted lines below. Use either words or symbols. Indicate the position of each chord, show whether it is major, minor, augmented or diminished, and name the prevailing key.

Bar 13 .... Key .... (4)

Bar 30 .... Key .... (4)

(b) Name two similarities and three differences between bars 1–4 and 24–28 (both marked ⌐‾‾‾‾‾‾‾‾‾‾‾⌐).

Similarities 1 .... (1)

2 .... (1)

Differences 1 .... (1)

2 .... (1)

3 .... (1)

(c) Mark **clearly** on the score, using the appropriate capital letter for identification, one example of each of the following. Also give the bar number(s) of each of your answers. The first answer is given.

In bars 1–16

A an instruction to play a note loud then immediately quiet. Bar ....7....

B an imperfect cadence in the tonic key. Bars .... (2)

C a modulation to the relative minor key. Bars .... (2)

D a melodic interval of a diminished 4th in
the right-hand part (circle the notes concerned). Bar .... (2)

(d) Complete the following statements:

(i) There is a pair of grace notes an octave apart in the right-hand part of bar .... (2)

(ii) In bars 16–19 (marked L‾‾‾‾‾‾‾‾‾‾‾‾‾‾‾⌐) the left hand repeats the melody previously

played by the right hand in bars .... but this time it is a(n) .... lower. (2)

There is one different note and the letter name of this note is .... (1)

(e) From the list below, underline the name of the most likely composer of this extract.

J. S. Bach   Schubert   Wagner   (1)

5 Look at the extract printed opposite, which is from Rimsky-Korsakov's suite *Le Coq d'or*, and then answer the questions below.

(a) Give the meaning of:

Piatti .... (2)

div. (bar 3, second violins) .... (2)

gliss. (bar 8, harp) .... (2)

(b) (i) Write out the parts for clarinets in bars 3–4 as they would sound at concert pitch and using the given clef.

(3)

(ii) Write out the parts for horns in bar 8 as they would sound at concert pitch and using the given clefs.

(4)

(c) Complete the following statements:

(i) A woodwind instrument playing in this extract which sounds an octave higher than written is the .... (2)

(ii) A non-transposing standard orchestral double-reed instrument which does *not* play in this extract is the .... (2)

(d) Describe fully the numbered and bracketed harmonic intervals *sounding* in each of the following bars:

1 bar 1, first clarinet and first flute .... (2)

2 bar 8, cellos and violas .... (2)

(e) Answer TRUE or FALSE to the following statements:

(i) The first horn and violas *sound* at the same pitch in bar 7. .... (2)

(ii) The notes played by the horns in bar 6 form a minor triad in first inversion. .... (2)

BLANK PAGE

Theory Paper Grade 6   2011   S

Duration 3 hours

TOTAL MARKS
100

Candidates should answer all FIVE questions.
Write your answers on this paper – no others will be accepted.
Answers must be written clearly and neatly – otherwise marks may be lost.

1 Answer ONE section only, (a) or (b).

15

EITHER

(a) Indicate ONE chord at each of the places marked * to accompany the following melody. You may do so by writing roman numerals or any other recognized method of notation between the staves, OR by writing notes on the staves which provide a proper harmonic structure; but use only ONE of these methods.

Traditional Flemish Melody (adapted)

OR

(b) Complete the bass line and add a suitable figured bass as necessary, *from the fourth quaver of bar 2*, at the places marked ∗ in this passage. If you wish to use a $\frac{5}{3}$ chord, leave the space under the asterisk blank, but $\frac{5}{3}$ chords *must* be shown when used as part of a $\frac{6}{4}\frac{5}{3}$ progression or when chromatic alteration is required.

Handel, Aria from *Alexander's Feast* (adapted)

2 Writing for four-part voices (SATB) or keyboard, realize this figured bass. Assume that all chords are $\frac{5}{3}$ unless otherwise shown.

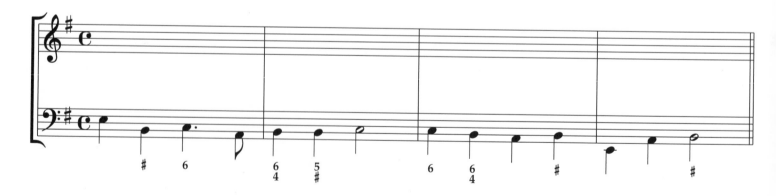

(a) Continue this opening to form a complete melody for unaccompanied clarinet (at concert pitch). It should end with a modulation to the dominant and should be between eight and ten bars long. Add performance directions as appropriate and write the complete melody on the staves below.

OR

(b) Continue this opening for unaccompanied cello to make a complete piece of not less than eight bars in length. You may make any modulation or modulations that you wish, or none if you prefer. Add performance directions as appropriate and write the complete melody on the staves below.

4 Look at the extract printed opposite, which is from the voice parts of Mozart's *Missa longa*, K. 262, and then answer the questions below.

(a) Identify the chord marked * in bar 10 (*ignoring the ornament*) by writing on the dotted lines below. Use either words or symbols. Indicate the position of the chord, show whether it is major, minor, augmented or diminished, and name the prevailing key.

Chord .... Key .... (4)

(b) Complete the following statements:

   (i) A male voice pitched between bass and tenor is called a .... (2)

   (ii) The extract passes twice through the dominant key:

   once in bar(s) .... and then in bar(s) .... (2)

   (iii) Tutti (e.g. bar 1) means .... (2)

(c) Write out in full the soprano part of bar 10, *without the words*, as you think it should be sung.

(3)

(d) Mark **clearly** on the score, using the appropriate capital letter for identification, one example of each of the following. Also give the bar number of each of your answers. The first answer is given.

From bar 5 onwards

   A a place where the alto part sounds a minor 3rd higher than the soprano part (circle the notes concerned). Bar ....8....

   B an upper auxiliary note in the soprano part (circle the note concerned). Bar .... (2)

   C a harmonic interval of an augmented 4th between the soprano and tenor parts (circle the notes concerned). Bar .... (2)

   D a place where the bass and tenor parts sing a note in unison (circle the notes concerned). Bar .... (2)

(e) The opening motif in bar 1 of the bass part (marked ⌐‾‾‾‾‾⌐) occurs throughout the extract. Give one example of its occurrence *in each of the other three voices* by naming the voice and bar number(s).

Voice .... Bar(s) .... (2)

Voice .... Bar(s) .... (2)

Voice .... Bar(s) .... (2)

5 Look at the extract printed opposite, which is from an overture by Bruckner, and then answer the questions below.

(a) Give the meaning of:

Un poco meno mosso .... (3)

ben legato .... (2)

(b) (i) Write out the parts for clarinets in bar 9 as they would sound at concert pitch.

(4)

(ii) Write out the parts for horns in bar 12 as they would sound at concert pitch and using the given clef.

(4)

(c) Complete the following statements:

(i) A standard orchestral double-reed instrument, *not* playing in this extract, that normally uses the bass clef is the .... (2)

(ii) There is a melodic interval of a diminished 7th in the first violin part in bar .... (2)

(d) Describe fully the numbered and bracketed harmonic intervals *sounding* in each of the following bars:

1 bar 5, violas and first horn .... (2)

2 bar 11, first clarinet and second oboe .... (2)

(e) Answer TRUE or FALSE to each of the following statements:

(i) The first and second violins play the same notes sounding an octave apart in bars 7–8. .... (2)

(ii) The second violins and violas play a note in unison in bar 3. .... (2)